The Karl Jenkins
Piano Album

BOOSEY & HAWKES

Boosey & Hawkes Music Publishers Ltd
www.boosey.com

Published by Boosey & Hawkes Music Publishers Ltd
Aldwych House
71–91 Aldwych
London
WC2B 4HN

www.boosey.com

Cover picture: Rhossili Bay, Gower Peninsular. © NTPL/Joe Cornish

ISMN 979-0-060-11762-6
ISBN 978-0-85162-540-9

Fifth impression 2019

Printed by Halstan:
Halstan UK, 2–10 Plantation Road, Amersham, Bucks, HP6 6HJ. United Kingdom
Halstan DE, Weißliliengasse 4, 55116 Mainz. Germany

Music origination by Max Knight and Andy Keenan

Contents • Inhalt • Sommaire

Pie Jesu

from Requiem

KARL JENKINS

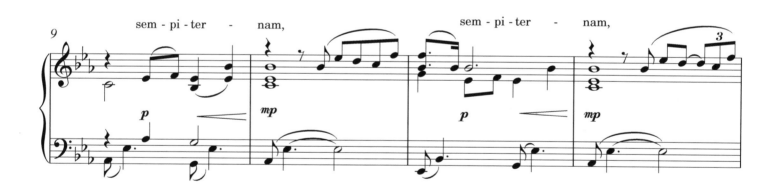

In paradisum
from Requiem

KARL JENKINS

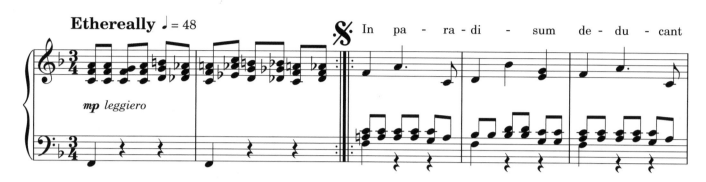

In paradisum deducant te angeli,
In tuo adventu suscipiant te martyres,
et perducant te in civitatem sanctam Jerusalem.

Chorus angelorum te suscipiat.
Et cum Lazaro quondam paupere
aeternam habeas requiem.

Ave verum

KARL JENKINS

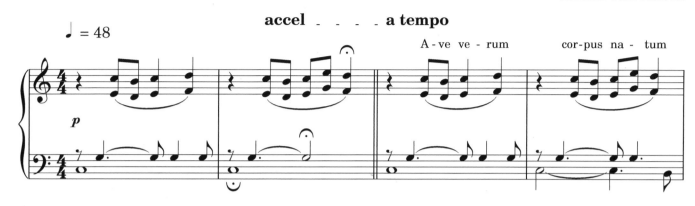

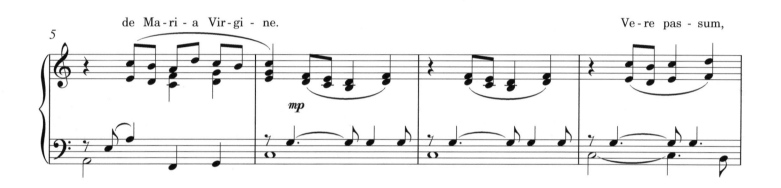

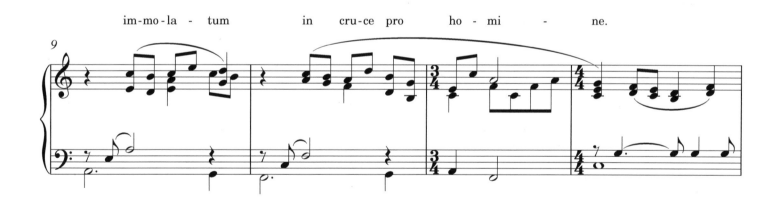

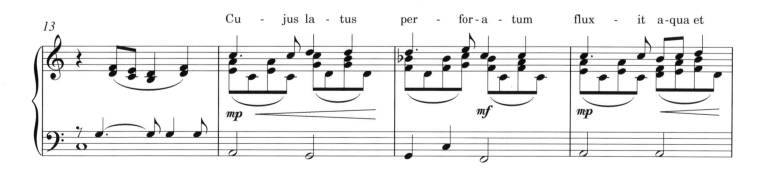

molto rall

Benedictus

from The Armed Man: A Mass for Peace

KARL JENKINS

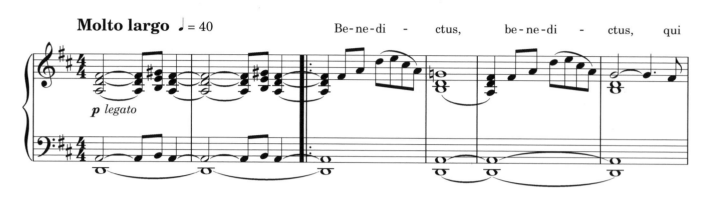

Agnus Dei
from The Armed Man: A Mass for Peace

KARL JENKINS

The girl with the green eyes

CAROL BARRATT

KARL JENKINS

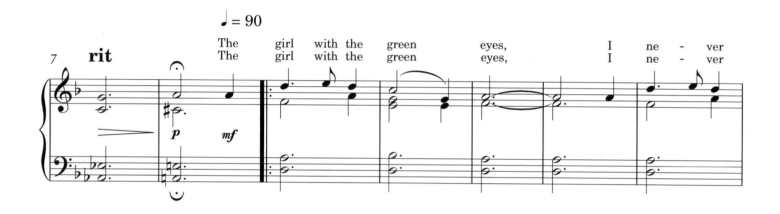

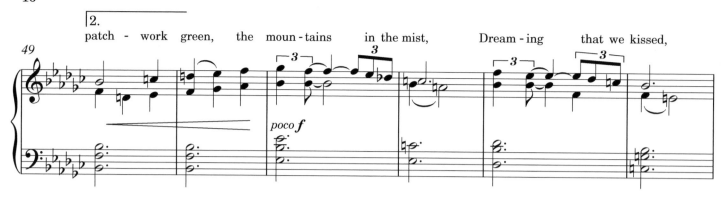

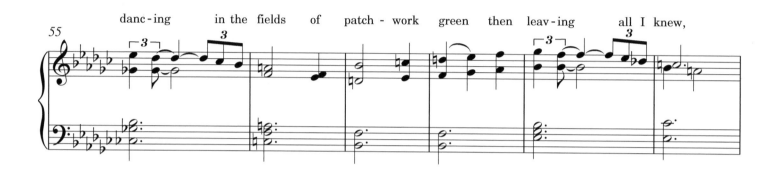

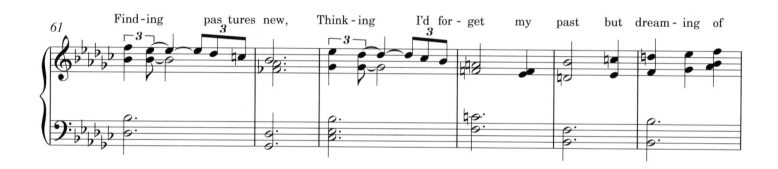

Antema Africana

from Kiri sings Karl

KARL JENKINS

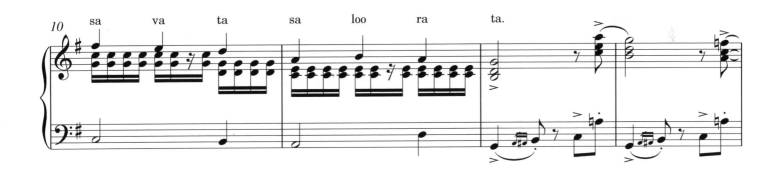

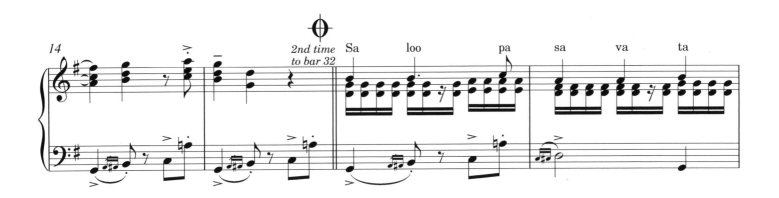

Y Cyfrinwyr
The Mystics
from Kiri sings Karl

English words by CAROL BARRATT
Welsh translation by GRAHAME DAVIES

KARL JENKINS

3. And the Mystics came to tell,
   came to tell us what to do.
   In the glories of nature,
   in the silence of prayer
   we can find our true spirit,
   all the answers are there.

3. A'r Cyfrinwyr ddaeth i ddweud,
   ddweud yr hyn sydd raid i ni.
   Yng ngogoniant byd natur,
   yn ein gweddïau mud
   mae tangnefedd i'n hysbryd
   mae'r atebion i gyd.

Paya paya

from Kiri sings Karl

KARL JENKINS

Cantus – Song of Tears

from Adiemus: Cantata Mundi

KARL JENKINS

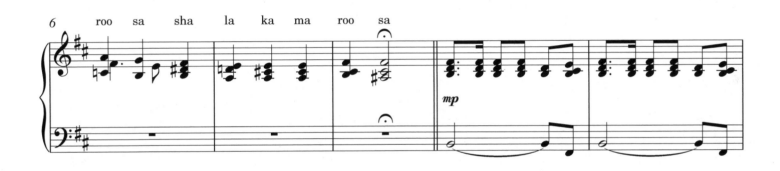

Theme from *Palladio*

KARL JENKINS

DS al Coda

CODA

Hymn
from Adiemus: Songs of Sanctuary

KARL JENKINS

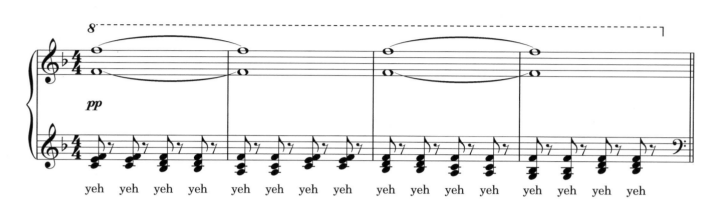

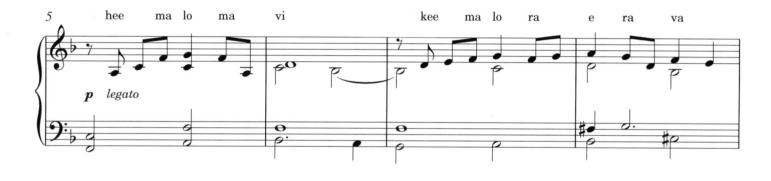

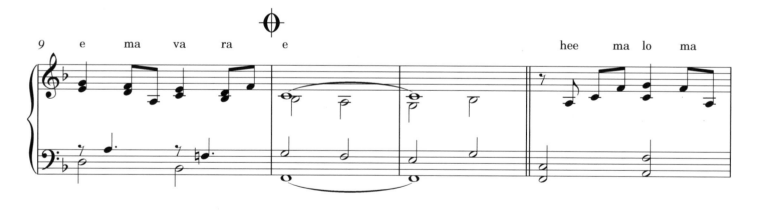

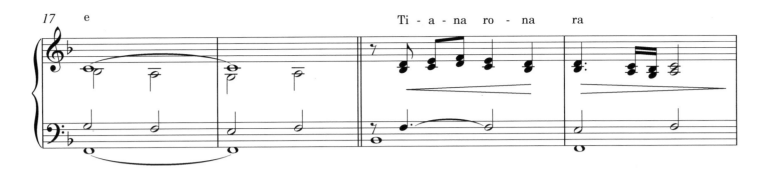

DC al Coda

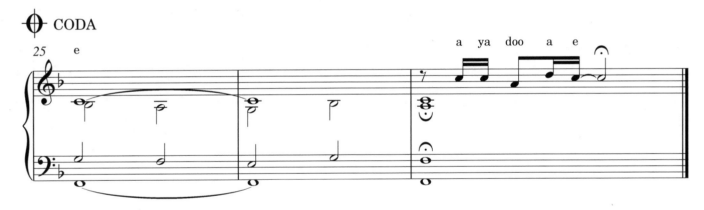

Cantilena
from The Journey (The Best of Adiemus)

KARL JENKINS

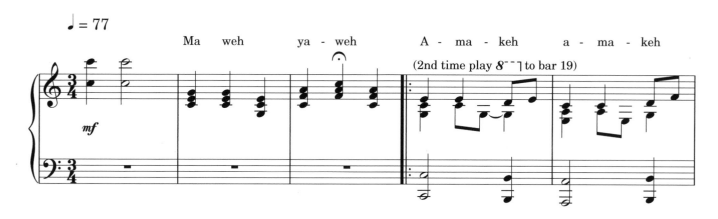

Bendigedig

Blessed

from Adiemus: Vocalise

KARL JENKINS

KARL JENKINS:PIANO

Music from *The Armed Man, Adiemus* and more
Intimate and spiritually uplifting classics reimagined for solo piano

• Cantilena • Benedictus • White Water • Palladio • Hymn • Lullay • The Prayer: Laudamus te • Adiemus • Agnus Dei
• Quirky Blue • Pie Jesu • Ave verum • Healing Light: a Celtic Prayer • I'll Make Music • In paradisum • And the Mother did Weep
• The Girl with the Green Eyes • Canción plateada • Only Heavenly Music • Lacrimosa • Kyrie • The Mystics

ISMN 979-0-060-13612-2
ISBN 978-1-78454-526-0

Recorded by Karl Jenkins on Decca CD 4817817

Boosey & Hawkes Music Publishers Ltd
www.boosey.com

Ad 535